This Little Tiger book belongs to:

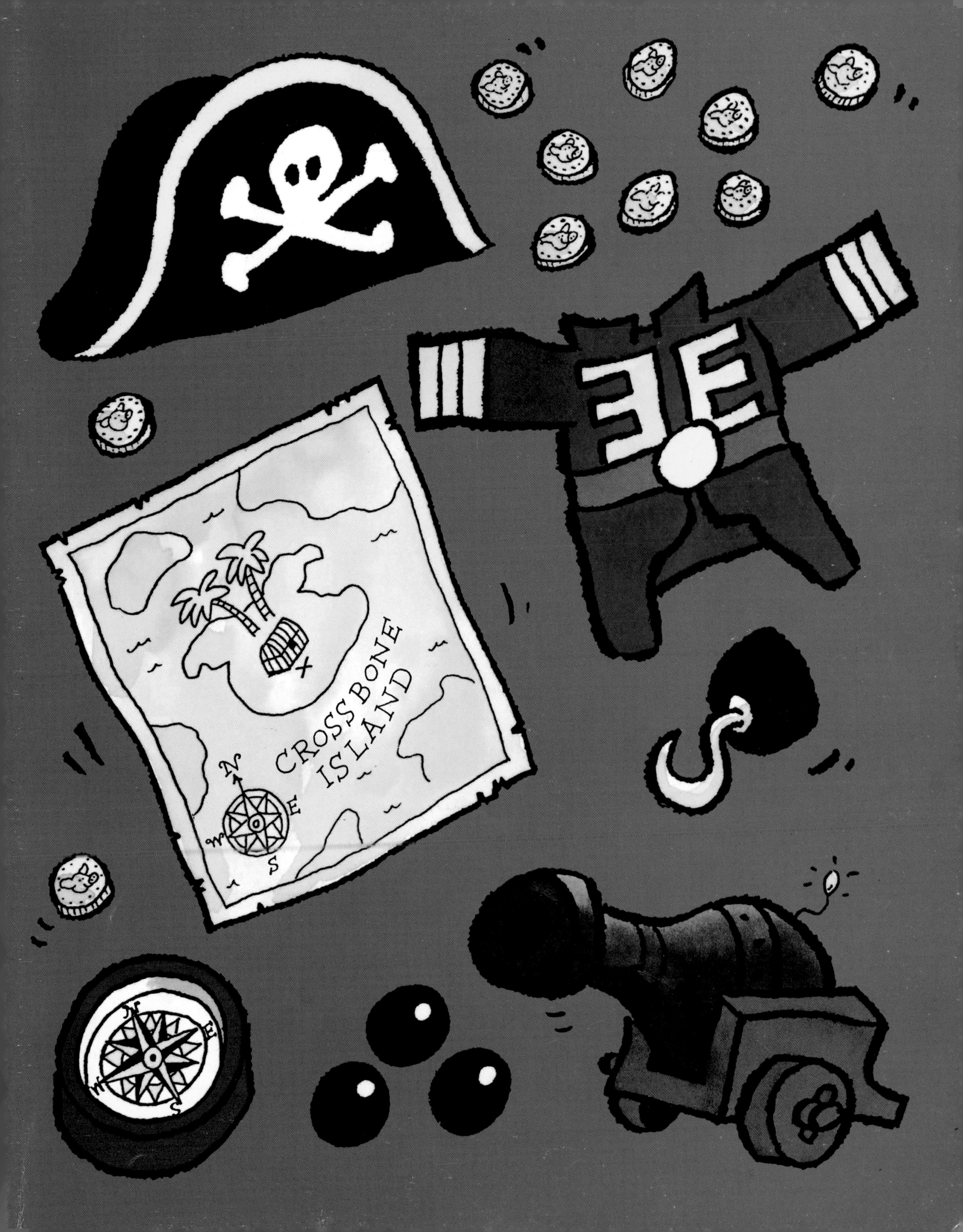
CROSSBONE
ISLAND

For Paul

the nicest pirate we know

LITTLE TIGER PRESS
An imprint of Magi Publications
1 The Coda Centre, 189 Munster Road, London SW6 6AW
www.littletigerpress.com
First published in Great Britain 2003
This edition published 2003

Printed in Malaysia by Tien Wah Press Pte
 · ISBN 1 85430 875 0
A CIP catalogue record for this book is
available from the British Library
2 4 6 8 10 9 7 5 3 1

Pirate PiggyWiggy

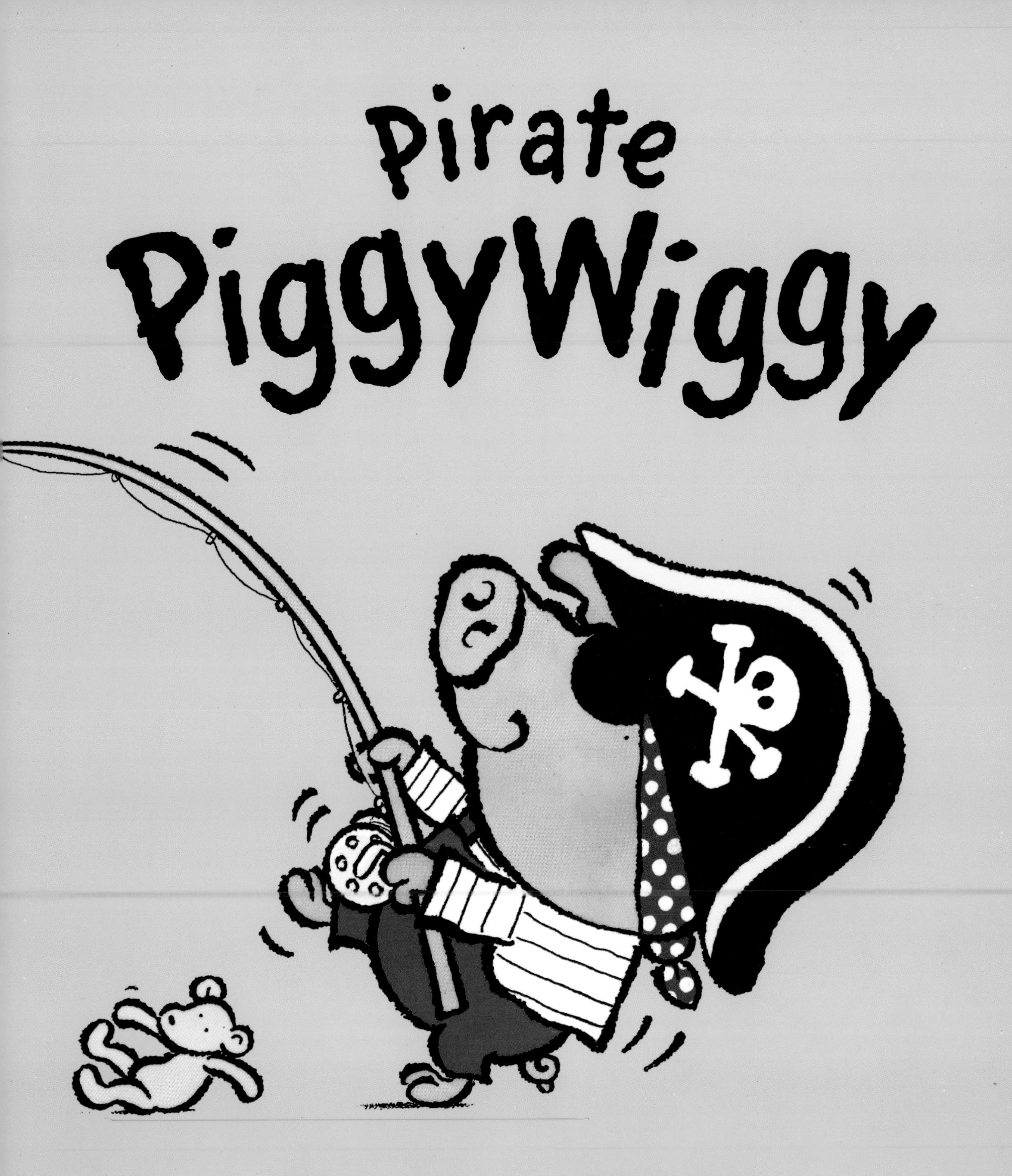

Christyan and Diane Fox

LITTLE TIGER PRESS

Sometimes when I sail my little boats, I dream of what it might be like to be a swashbuckling pirate!

"Ha-haaarrr!"

I would wear
a big black hat,
a patch over my eye
and have a parrot
on my shoulder...

My ship would be the finest that ever sailed the seven seas.

"Hoist the mainsail, Teddy!"
The Jolly Roger

On hot, sunny days
we could walk
the plank!

At night-time we could sit around the fire singing sea shanties....

"Yo-ho-ho!"

On Crossbone Island
we would search for
treasure.
CROSSBONE
ISLAND
N
W
E
S

Ten paces north...
eight paces south...

Shiver-me-timbers,
X marks the spot!

CROSSBONE ISLAND
N
W
E
HERE BE TREASURE
THIS IS IT!
DIG HERE

Ha-haaarr,
pieces of eight!

The richest treasure
ever seen...

But we'd have to
sail back home again

to find the treasure
we love best!

More adventures for young readers from Little Tiger Press

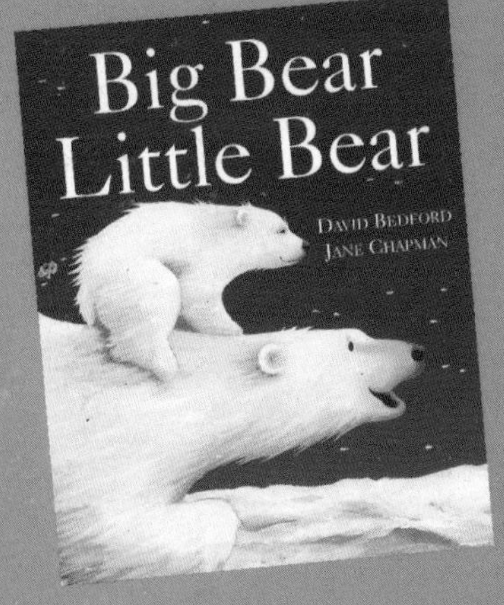

What's the Opposite, PiggyWiggy?

What Shape is That, PiggyWiggy?

For information regarding any of the above titles or for our full catalogue, please contact us: Little Tiger Press, 1 The Coda Centre, 189 Munster Road, London SW6 6AW, UK
Tel: 020 7385 6333 Fax: 020 7385 7333 e-mail: info@littletiger.co.uk www.littletigerpress.com